I SEE MYSELF IN PERFECT HEALTH

A visualisation for health book

by: **David Lawson**

Edited by Justin Carson

Illustrations by Bill Wyatt

A Starseed Book from Healing Workshops Press

First Printing September 1990

Cover Photography and Design by : Delilah Dyson
Photographs of David & Justin by : Marie Hyde
Typeset by : Justin Carson

ISBN 0 9516237 1 0

A CIP Catalogue record for this book is available from the British Library

Published by: **Healing Workshops Press**
PO Box 1678
London NW5 4EW

Phone 071 482 4049

Printed by Caldra House Limited, 23 Coleridge Street, Hove, Sussex BN3 5AB

Dedicated to Justin. Thank you for all your love, imagination and support and for all of the magic we create together on our healing journeys.

Thanks to Bill, Delilah and Marie for sharing their pictures and to all of our friends and participants for sharing in mine.

Special thanks to Louise L. Hay for her inspiration and continued support.

FOREWORD

I use visual images to illuminate my own meditations as well as to help others step more and more into their self-healing power. I have always found pleasure in combining visualisation techniques with positive thoughts, hands on healing and creative planning while leading individual healing sessions and group work.

I have often been asked to write down or record my ideas so that friends, clients and participants can continue with the images where I stop; using them as the basis for their own visual journeys as they take themselves to greater health and personal power. Here then is my first collection of creative daydreams for your use.

The visualisations in this book have come to me in a variety of ways, some are adaptations of ideas that I have collected as a participant of many self-development workshops while others have come to me through a process of direct channelling; simply from sitting quietly, clearing my mind and allowing my higher voice and the higher voices of others to speak through me.

Mostly, though, my visualisations are conceived as I guide people through healing meditations; a mixture of channelling and my own creative process. All of the images evolve through use and repaint themselves in different ways for the needs of each person or group that I work with.

There is no right or wrong way of using these images. Feel free to repaint them in any way that suits your needs and enjoy the many pleasures that visualisation can bring.

Your very good health!

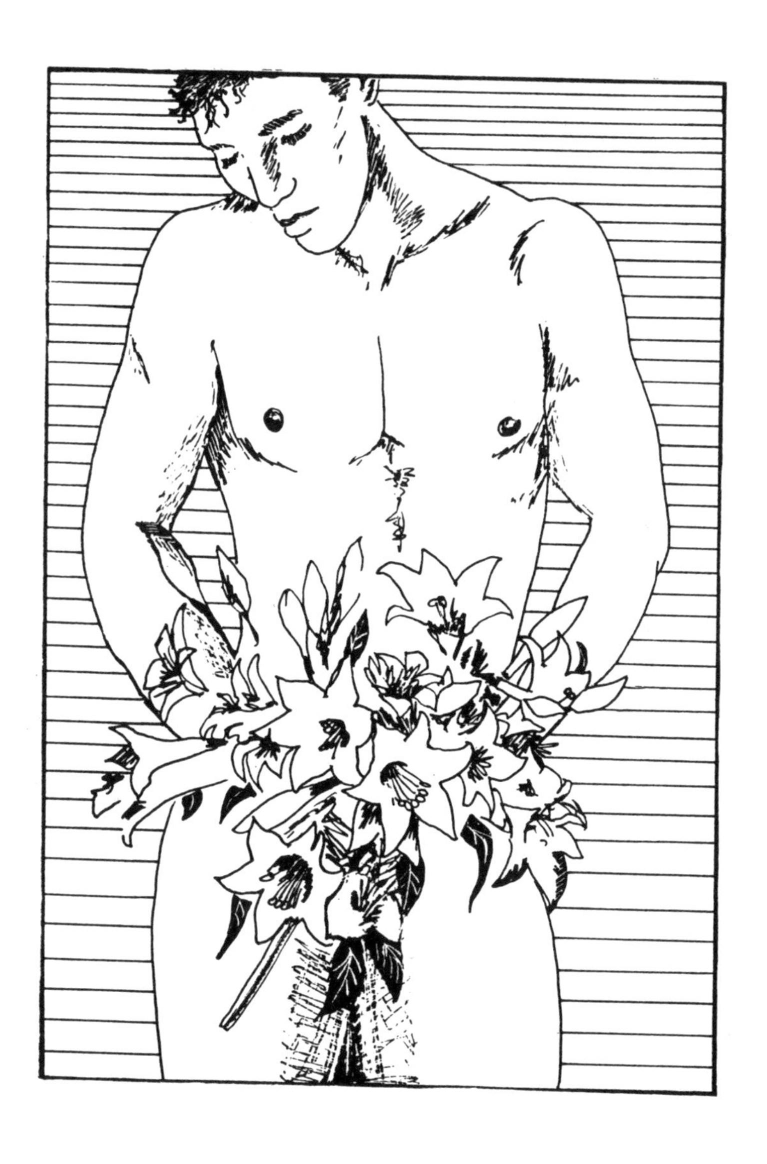

HOW TO USE THIS BOOK

This is a playbook for your imagination and your self-healing power.

There are 14 sections each divided into four pages.

The title of each section is a leading affirmation followed by some thoughts for meditation, visualisation exercises and then a visual affirmation line drawing.

The exercises presented are appropriate for women and men of all ages; they can be adapted for children to use too.

The only rule for using this book is to enjoy it.

Use it to help you relax

Each visualisation is designed to be used as part of your regular relaxation or meditation time. Taking ten or twenty minutes every day to close your eyes, breathe deeply and visualise is a pleasurable way to reduce stress.

Use it to Programme for your Health

Read through the book first to become acquainted with the feel of its layout and then either work through each Creative Daydream in turn or else concentrate on those areas that are most relevant to you.

At other times randomly open the book to an affirmation, image or exercise knowing that the page you have opened is exactly right for you at this time, and then either do the visualisation selected or hold the image or affirmation in your mind to create a shift in your way of thinking.

The exercises in this book are written to complement rather than replace standard medical practice and other methods of health care.

Use it to expand your mind and creativity

Visualisation will help you to train and release your innate creativity, helping you to add colour and imagination to everything you do. Exercising your thoughts in this way strengthens your connection to your higher mind and your personal power.

USING VISUALISATION

Visualisation is the use of mental images to create the experiences that we choose to have in our lives. Our minds are powerful; we can daydream away stress, create calm and peace, prevent illness, promote good health, speed up the recuperative process and in many cases heal every area of our lives.

Many have already discovered that the power of Creative Daydreams has a miraculous effect on their home environment, their career, their finances and their relationships. To change your world you begin by changing your thoughts, the rest follows naturally.

Visualisation and all positive thought techniques work directly on the most important relationship of all, the relationship we have with ourselves. How else can we create health and love in our lives if we don't see ourselves as healthy and lovable and deserving of these things?

This book has been written to sow seeds and be a starting point for your own imagination. Generally we all choose the images that work best for us. You are the source of your power and wisdom; you hold the key to positive change.

USING AFFIRMATIONS

'I see myself in perfect health' and 'I now create a healthy mind and body' are two examples of positive affirmations for health.

A positive affirmation is a phrase or thought that can be used to change our beliefs; ensuring that we are in the right frame of mind to create better and better things in our lives.

Our thoughts are powerful. What we think affects the way we are today and forms the reality of tomorrow. We cannot be happy, healthy and prosperous if we don't truly believe that all these things are available to us.

Affirmations are used to retrain our minds and discard old, learned patterns of thought that no longer serve us, replacing them with new thoughts that do. By affirming, we alter our beliefs to support our needs and desires, changing our reality accordingly.

All of the affirmations in this book can be used in this way and you may also like to make up some of your own that are particularly relevant to your health issues or your goals.

GUIDELINES FOR CREATING AND USING AFFIRMATIONS

(A) Affirmations need to be in the present tense. For example 'I NOW CREATE.....' or 'I AM ALWAYS .....' (present continuous). The reason for this is that if you affirm that something is going to happen or that it will happen then you are creating it in the future, and that is where it will stay, constantly out of reach. 'In three weeks I will be..........' will always stay three weeks away.

(B) Trust that your affirmation is true for you even if it couldn't be further from reality at this point in time. If you are very ill and things are looking bleak, then affirming that you are always in perfect health is going to create the right energy that will draw healing to you. This is not the same as denying what is happening to you or covering up your feelings; always acknowledge your current situation and then change the thoughts to change the reality.

(C) Your negative or limiting thoughts are the raw material for creating positive affirmations. Each negative thought contains the foundation for positive change and growth. 'I will never be free of back pain' can become `I easily release pain' or 'My back is free and healthy'.

(D) Affirmations can be written, typed, spoken aloud, sung, chanted and said to yourself in the mirror as well as being repeated over and over in your mind. Be creative and choose ways to use them that work best for you.

(E) Affirmations are meant to be fun.

SETTING THE SCENE

For all of the exercises in this book it is best to use a safe quiet place that is warm and comfortable. Minimise distractions by unplugging telephones, asking others not to disturb you and if necessary putting out the cat; although I meditate with mine. Use music in the background if it helps to relax you but make sure that it is calming and melodic and without lyrics that would fight for your attention.

Either sit with your back properly supported; making sure that your feet are firmly planted on the floor, or lie down on your back. Whatever you do keep your arms and legs, hands and feet uncrossed; keeping your body open and receptive.

Once you are comfortable with the techniques used, then you can practice them in many situations, but the above scenario is the easiest.

It is not important to follow every detail of the exercises exactly so just read them through a couple of times to familiarise yourself with their essence before settling down and trusting your mind to take care of the images perfectly for you. If it helps then make a tape recording of your voice guiding you through the visualisations and repeating the affirmations.

Some people have a natural ability to visualise in pictures while with others it comes with practice. Regardless of how your mind works, your intention is much more important than your capacity to get strong visual images. Just holding the concept, or the idea of the picture, in your mind is enough for these techniques to work for you.

If you allow your mind the freedom to play without trying too hard then you will be amazed by the results.

I SEE MYSELF IN PERFECT HEALTH

Everything we do starts with thought and intention whether conscious or unconscious. Each thought we have is pure energy.

Positive thoughts send a wave of bright positive energy into our bodies and into our lives.

Believing in health creates health, believing in peace creates peace.

Our thoughts are powerful.

Find a comfortable place to sit or lie. If you are sitting make sure that your back is properly supported and have your feet firmly planted on the floor. In all cases keep your arms and legs uncrossed and your body open.

Close your eyes and breathe three long, slow, deep, breaths and continue to breathe deeply and easily.

Imagine yourself naked, standing in front of a full length mirror. In your mind's eye make the mirror beautiful and shining. You can see every part of your body reflected. Particularly notice the reflection of your feet, your hips and your shoulders. Imagine yourself looking deeply into your eyes.

This is a picture of you as you really are; healthy, relaxed, happy, loved and peaceful. Every part of you is the perfect shape and size. Your face is beautiful, your skin bright and clear, your posture perfect.

If you are working through any physical challenge or disease you notice that you are completely healed and whole. If you have any emotional problems or tensions you see in your eyes and your posture that you are completely free of this. All stress and worry has been released, all burdens have fallen away from you. In your mind frequently repeat the words "I see myself in perfect health."

Repeat this exercise often. Not only as part of your regular relaxation or meditation time but also when you have a couple of minutes to spare around the home, at work or even during a train or bus journey.

I WASH AWAY ALL TENSION

Water is a very powerful image to use in creative daydreams, just thinking of it has a cleansing and refreshing effect on the mind, body and spirit. It helps to dissipate any negative thoughts and feelings that we might have accumulated from other people or from our environment and leaves us clear and healthy.

The exercise that follows can be practised in two ways; as the pure visualisation described or as a part of the physical experience of taking a bath.

Everything we do, no matter how ordinary, can be created as sacred and special, this then becomes a practical affirmation of our own power, health and beauty.

Sit or lie down, keeping your body open and receptive.

Breathe deeply and slowly into your abdomen and count backwards from 9 to 0. Imagine yourself relaxing more and more as you breathe and count down. It may help to go through your body, starting with your feet and ending with your scalp, relaxing each area in turn. Be comfortable.

In your mind see yourself in the most beautiful bathroom you have ever seen. Notice the colours and the shapes. It is warm, clean and safe.

See yourself moving towards the bath and turning on the taps, seeing and hearing the bright water tumble into it. Turning back to the room imagine yourself lighting candles, putting out flowers or crystals or other beautiful objects that inspire you.

Imagine opening cupboards to choose large, soft towels in colours that are healing for you and laying out clothes in the same colours, that you know will be wonderful to wear. When everything is perfect see yourself turning off the taps and stepping into the bath. Feel the water soothe and relax you as you settle into it. Hold an image of yourself for a while being cleansed and recharged in this beautiful environment.

If you have a particular physical or emotional challenge to work on or if you would like to release any negative experiences or feelings, then during the bath imagine that next to you is a basket of dried wild herbs. See yourself taking a handful of herbs and casting them into the water which bubbles for a moment before becoming the perfect healing colour for you. As it clears, see and feel your problem healing and releasing. If there are many things you would like to work on then repeat this as many times as you choose before completing your bath and emerging refreshed.

Dry yourself off and adorn yourself in your magical clothes which will continue to keep you safe and protected after your bath.

I AM GROUNDED IN HEALTH

The earth and all natural things are a constant inspiration and a ready source of healing energy and balance.

Surrounding ourselves with plants, pottering in the garden and going for long walks through the trees are all ways of discharging stress and disease.

The earth has the power to draw down negative energy and discharge it harmlessly whether you enjoy being out and about in nature or just picture yourself being so.

This exercise is a very useful tool for general healing and relaxation as well as being extremely beneficial if you are feeling listless. It is good too if you travel around a great deal or if you find it hard to put your ideas into practice. It is particularly recommended for city dwellers.

Sit or lie comfortably and breathe deeply and then imagine that in the centre of each foot there is a tingling sensation, and in your mind's eye notice that you are growing beautiful white roots through your instep. The roots develop slowly at first but soon grow faster and stronger.

If you are indoors imagine the floor beneath you melting a little to allow your roots to pass through it and as you continue to breathe deeply see them growing downwards through every layer of the building towards the earth below.

Feel the sensation as your roots touch and then move through the top soil before moving down through the layers of rock towards the centre of the earth. At the earth's core imagine a glow of warm (not hot) red energy and see your roots begin to drink in this redness and draw some of it up through the rock strata towards your body.

In your mind begin to fill your body with this red earth energy from your feet upwards until it permeates your being entirely and see yourself warmed and relaxed by it.

See any tension, fear, disease or imbalance being melted by the redness of the earth's energy and being drawn down and out into the ground naturally and harmlessly. Concentrate particularly on your areas of need, and watch as these parts of your body are soothed and healed.

Once you have completed the process see your roots shrinking back into your body again leaving a little glow of energy in your heart and any other part of you that you choose. Try this exercise outside too and notice if it feels any different.

I
OPEN UP TO
HEALTH

Our bodies are filled with energy centres, or chakras. Many of these are quite small but there are seven larger main chakras at different points along the spinal column and in the head.

Some people see these energy centres as wheels of coloured light constantly spinning; sometimes large and open, and at other times small and closed.

Whether we believe in chakras or not, seeing these areas of the body balance and clean themselves has a healing effect on every area of our lives.

This exercise is best done when you are on your own or in a safe environment. It is not for public transport or any situation where there are a lot of people around you.

Settle. Open your body and breathe deeply, then taking your attention to the base of your spine and the area of your groin imagine that there is a tiny flower sitting there still in bud. It is the deep red colour associated with this energy centre.

As you breathe you see the bud touched and warmed with golden sunlight which causes its petals to begin to open and grow. You are aware of its beauty. As you watch the flower grows bigger, bolder and brighter, opening and growing in each moment. You notice that this flower is clean and perfectly formed.

Repeat this process with all the other main energy centres, moving up your body as follows:

In your stomach see an orange flower opening.
At your solar plexus see a yellow flower opening.
At the level of your heart, a green flower, or green leaves.
In your throat a bright blue flower.
At the centre of your forehead a dark blue or indigo flower.
At the top, or slightly above your head, imagine a violet or white flower.

When all of these flowers are open and bright, take your attention to any one of them that you feel could be even brighter or stronger. See it bathed in more light and make any changes that you might wish.

Always complete the exercise by seeing each flower from the top of your body to the bottom gently closing again, as flowers do at night time, going within, safe and protected. If at any time you feel too open and vulnerable then you can choose to see each flower closing up to keep your energy bright and safe.

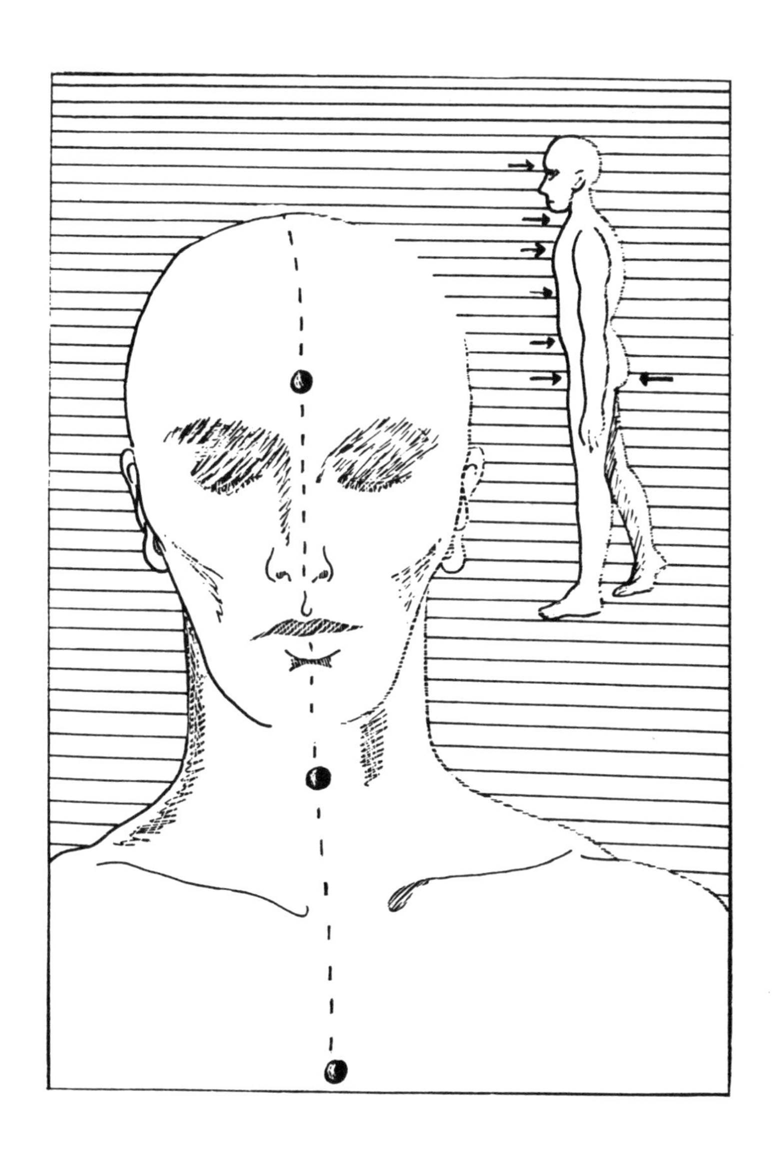

I AM ALWAYS IN THE PINK

Colour is pure vibrational energy.

The colours we surround ourselves with have a dramatic effect on our minds, bodies and emotions. Wearing a particular colour can be healing and empowering and have an influence on how we are received by others.

Trust yourself to instinctively choose those colours that you need at any given time in your life. Use colour to balance yourself physiologically and psychologically.

It is not essential to know what qualities each colour has because no two people will be effected in the same way by the same hues, but notice how you feel when you wear different colours or when you are in a room painted in a particular shade.

Visualising or imagining a colour is as powerful as wearing it, perhaps even more so.

Make yourself comfortable and breathe deeply.

Imagine yourself drawing on an endless source of pure light energy from the world around you. You are able to breathe it in directly to every part of your body.

Starting at your feet, imagine them fill with this light and as you draw it into every cell you see it becoming the perfect healing colour and vibration for this part of your body, relaxing and charging you up with power and vitality. Regenerating and revitalising.

Breathe light into your ankles and notice its colour, it may be the same as before, a slightly different shade or completely different. Whatever the colour is, know that it is perfect for this part of your body.

Continue this process with your legs, and then upwards until your whole body is filled with its perfect healing colour; hold this image of yourself as you breathe and relax more and more.

Repeat this exercise often. It is especially good to do just before going to sleep. The combination of colours and shades is rarely the same twice because our needs are constantly changing.

An alternative version of this exercise is to imagine yourself standing at the end of a rainbow. Picture your body drinking in coloured light directly from it.

When your body is filled with colour, award yourself a crock of gold for good measure.

I GO BEYOND MY LIMITATIONS TO CREATE HEALTH

The element of air is associated with our mental faculties and higher consciousness.

Using air images in visualisations helps us to clear the mind and sharpen our thinking as well as creating more freedom in our lives and building our connection to the Divine.

To see ourselves rising through the air, floating or flying is a very effective way of freeing up when we get stuck with limited thoughts or outmoded beliefs. From this elevated perspective it is easier to appreciate the greater picture and the purpose of our lives.

Lie down on your back for this visualisation.

Picture your body filling up with coloured healing light as in the previous exercise. Notice the colour in each part of you before visualising this energy building and expanding.

Soon there is so much colour that you are able to spread a layer of this healing energy out beneath you and you feel it cushioning each part of your body. See the different colours begin to weave themselves into each other and allow them to form the most beautiful patterns you have ever seen.

As the patterns become solid, notice that your coloured light has become a warm, soft magic carpet for you to lie on. Take a little time to relax and drop your body into its loving support before letting it lift you gently upwards.

Knowing that your will controls your journey, see the carpet carrying you higher and higher, all obstacles such as the ceiling and roof melt to allow you through. See yourself moving through the sky and out to the far reaches of the atmosphere.

Allow your thoughts to wander and take yourself on a magical healing journey through the cosmos. Be playful and trust your higher mind to show you beautiful things and to inspire you with new ideas. Hear any words of wisdom that are whispered to you and let yourself be touched by new feelings that send your senses reeling. Look down too on the world you have left behind and notice what you see.

When you feel complete, see yourself travelling back. The carpet cradling you as it brings you down to earth again. If you feel at all light headed you might like to imagine yourself anchoring your carpet or see yourself firmly planting your feet.

I
CONTAIN
POWER
AND
HEALING ENERGY

We contain the potential to be anything we want to be, do anything we want to do and achieve any ambition or goal. We are all infinitely wise, powerful, creative, expressive and gifted.

Visualising ourselves filled with power in any form whether for health, love or material success helps put us in touch with our potential, connecting us to our innate wisdom, our passion for living and our ability to heal ourselves.

Sit or lie in a comfortable position and breathe deeply.

Imagine that you are able to stand outside of yourself and look at your body. In your mind's eye see the position of every part of you. Your legs and arms, your feet, knees, hips, spine, shoulders, and head. When you have a clear picture, allow the image to go out of focus and see it blur and change.

Slowly see the image becoming more solid again and notice that your body has become a container made of clear shining crystal. Every line and shape of your body is cut in crystal, perfect and beautiful.

Imagine too that it is possible for you to pass drops of beautiful blue healing liquid energy through the top of your head; the most beautiful blue you have ever seen, in the form of liquid light or liquid crystal.

Drop by drop the liquid passes through, forming a channel of blue that moves down through your body to your feet. See this energy filling your feet and then slowly moving up to fill every part of your body. Filling up to the level of your ankles, your knees, your hips, your groin, your stomach, solar plexus, heart, throat, down your shoulders arms and hands, and finally filling up to the top of your head. Even imagine that every hair on your head is a tiny crystalline tube to be filled with healing power.

For a while, hold an image of yourself completely filled with this vibrant energy and know that it is charging you up with health.

Next, imagine yourself releasing all negative thoughts, bad experiences or undesirable relationships into the blue liquid as if they were clouds of black ink being squirted into the blueness.

See the blue becoming momentarily dull as the black spreads through and then imagine the blue liquid in your body digesting the black clouds until they have all been cleared easily away.

Notice now that the blue is brighter, stronger and clearer than ever before, and when you feel fully refreshed and revitalised by the blue energy, allow yourself to gently return to full awareness and open your eyes.

MY BODY IS FLEXIBLE

Laughter is a great healer.

There are many stories of people who have laughed themselves back to health. Laughter can discharge tension and fear, release bitterness and guide us to forgiveness.

Humour, no matter how irreverent, empowers thoughts and ideas to make them more memorable and effective. We can use it to add sparkle to our affirmations and visualisations.

The following exercise is one that is favoured by my partner, Justin, who has a wonderful ability to stop me taking anything too seriously.

Imagine that you have a team of tiny maintenance men and women moving around the inside of your body. They are dressed in overalls and carry oil cans, polishing cloths and spanners. Watch as they go about their allotted tasks, perhaps whistling cheerfully and tunelessly as they make their adjustments.

Visualise these workers as they oil your joints and work with their spanners to loosen any area that has become stiff, tense or painful.

They may cluster together to remove any larger obstructions or put their combined weight against anything that initially refuses to budge, before carrying off all rubbish in their sacks leaving your body completely free of debris.

The attention does not cease until every area of your body is free and relaxed. Make sure you see them regularly servicing the joints and massaging the muscles of your neck or any other area that regularly gets tight.

As well as general tension or tightness this is a good exercise to use for arthritis, specific injuries or if you are feeling mentally stuck.

It is also useful to visualise yourself moving any area of your body that is stiff and painful and that you might have difficulty moving, before gently exercising it. Pause for some deep breaths and then repeat the process.

OIL

MY IMMUNE SYSTEM FUNCTIONS PERFECTLY

Belief in our ability to develop illness not only allows for it but actively encourages it.

Many of us are open to catching colds, flu and whatever is going around because we believe that sooner of later we will fall prey to that particular infection.

For many of us, becoming ill is easier than asking for time off from work to rest, have some emotional space or deal with other interests or needs. Certainly in either a home or work environment where 'everyone else has got it', it is not easy to stay well when we are surrounded by such a strong collective belief in illness.

Of course, if we are ill, then we need to have the good grace to surrender to it rather than battling on regardless like a martyr, but it is important to ask ourselves exactly why we have created this situation and remember that we always have a choice.

Most of us know the concept of psychosomatic illness, and understanding how powerful our minds are, we have the option instead to consider psychosomatic wellness and choose perfect health for ourselves.

Constantly affirming our health is the best way to stay healthy.

The following exercises are good for preventing colds and flu as well as for diseases of the auto-immune system.

To put it simply, our blood is made up of a variety of red and white cells. Red cells deal with transporting energy and waste around the body and white cells deal with fighting infection.

Different white cells have different jobs, some ingest foreign matter, some act as dustmen to cart it all away and others plug the holes when we cut ourselves.

A) Picture your white cells as circus strongmen and imagine them building up and flexing their muscles. Perhaps they take a break every so often to eat high protein meals served to them by waiters who are the red blood cells.

B) See your white cells as a multitude of cleaners going around with their dusters and vacuum cleaners effortlessly fulfilling their function of making sure that everything is kept spotlessly clean.

C) Imagine your white cells relaxing under sun ray lamps, only instead of getting brown they get stronger, whiter and brighter.

I GROW IN STRENGTH AND RECEIVE SUPPORT

Movement enhances health and strength. Correct bodily exercise promotes healing, raises physical and mental energy and prevents disease.

Just as our bodies are able to move externally there are constant movements of energy inside of us. Cells die and new ones are formed to replace them, our brains send messages pulsing to every area of the body and the muscles of our stomachs are always expanding and contracting in the process of digestion.

Visualising a movement of light or energy inside us helps to exercise our natural internal movements and clear any blockages or restrictions.

The following exercise is particularly good for anyone who suffers from back pain or any postural problems.

Lie down on your back with your hands and arms stretched out wide but without straining. Keep your body as relaxed as possible and remember to breathe deeply.

Imagine a pulse of light continually moving from your left foot and up your left leg, passing through your knee joint and your left hip.

From your hip see it move to the base of your spine and then up your backbone to your neck where it changes direction to move across your right shoulder.

From your shoulder see the light continue to pulse along your right arm and out through your right hand. Imagine it clearing any pain on its path, balancing and recharging your body wherever it passes.

As you become comfortable with this image see the light arc or loop from your right hand all the way across your head to your left hand and see it pass through you in the opposite direction.

From your left hand see it pulse up your left arm and shoulder, moving into your neck and down your spine, again clearing away any pain as it goes.

See it passing down through your right hip and right leg and out through your foot, dumping any pain and tension harmlessly beneath your feet where it melts away into nothing.

Practice visualising this as a continuous movement and picture this pulse of light moving through you at all times to release tension and fear.

Halfway through the exercise, imagine this glow of power solidifying into energetic string and envisage yourself tightening or loosening the string at the bottom of each foot to balance, release and adjust the position of your spine.

When these adjustments have been made, see the energy begin to flow again. Perceive yourself as naturally balanced and peaceful.

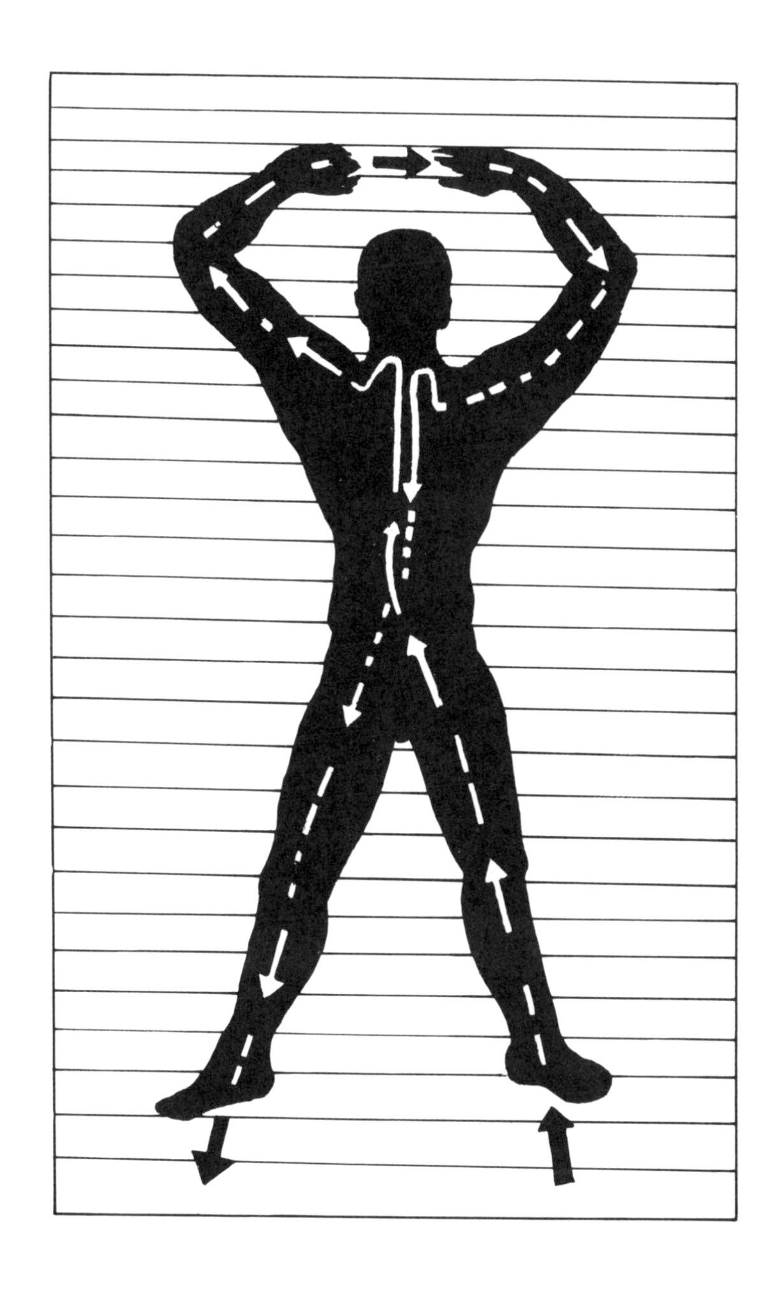

I BREATHE IN HEALTH AND VIBRANT ENERGY

Breathing deeply and slowly is an essential element of all relaxation and visualisation exercises. It immediately connects us to our body and our feelings, sending energy to those areas that need healing.

The use of the breath in conjunction with positive thoughts and images puts us in touch with our own natural rhythms as well as the rhythm and flow of the universe. In short, it connects us to our body's innate knowledge of how to balance and recharge itself.

This is a good exercise for building energy and vitality. It is particularly useful for conditions that deplete such as Myalgic Encephalomyelitis (M.E.) which is also known as Post-viral fatigue syndrome.

Lie on your back and breathe deeply.

Imagine that on each side of your neck you have gills like a fish through which you can breathe in healing light and energy.

In your thoughts see a golden ray of light come down from the atmosphere to touch you on the neck, and as you breathe air into your lungs you also breathe this light straight into your neck.

You breathe the light down through your body and your legs towards your feet. See the light moving out of your toes to arc back up over your body towards your head, either as one stream of gold moving above you, of if you prefer, two streams of gold each moving up one side of you.

Picture this light moving in through the top of your head and down into the neck where it connects up with the new energy coming in, and once combined it moves down the body again even brighter and stronger than before. See it as a continuous circuit of golden light building up more and more with every breath you take.

Repeat to yourself "I am filled with vibrant energy".

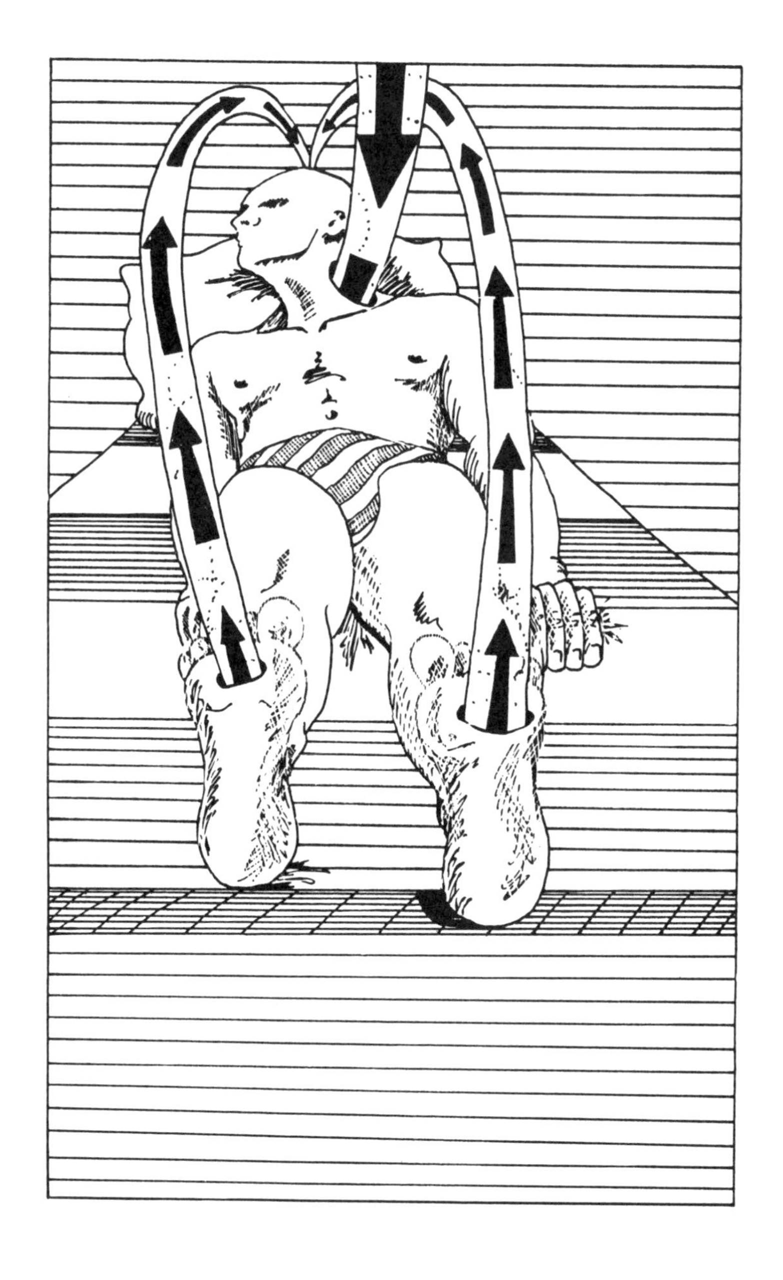

HEALTH IS A PEACEFUL PLACE

Our inner world is a limitless place potentially filled with magic, adventure, peace and harmony.

What we create inside ourselves ultimately creates the world around us. If we are living in chaos, going inside to the part of us that is peaceful and tranquil and building on that with our thoughts is the best way to begin calming our environment.

In your mind's eye, see yourself being transported to a safe place. It may be somewhere that you already know, somewhere you have lived or visited, or perhaps some place you loved as a child.

Alternatively, this place could be somewhere new that you create with your mind and your heart. It might be constant or it can change every time you repeat this exercise. It does not matter as long as you feel happy and completely safe there.

Here are some examples you might try:-

A deserted beach on a paradise island surrounded by palm trees and tropical flowers.

A walled garden filled with flowers, fragrant herbs and sunshine. Perhaps you will find a clear running stream in which to dangle your feet.

A warm wooden shelter in a forest of pine trees and fern.

A cavern filled with crystals that glitter and shine as the light catches them.

A room draped in silk and filled with the sound of soft chimes.

See as many details as you can, paint the colours, smell the smells, touch, taste and hear your safe place. Breathe and allow the feeling of calm to permeate your mind and body.

Before completing this exercise, imagine that this safe feeling transmutes into coloured light and see it spreading out to surround your body and fill every part of your home and life.

I FILL MYSELF WITH VIBRANT ENERGY

There is no limit to the personal power that we can create for ourselves.

Real personal power is not something that we build or acquire to the detriment of those around us. Being powerful is about everyone winning.

One person stepping more directly into their light and freedom is inspiring and empowering for others.

Imagine as you breathe that you draw down a column of white light energy from the atmosphere. This light moves down towards you through the sky and through any physical obstructions smoothly and swiftly.

This energy pauses for a moment just above your head before bathing the whole of your body in whiteness. See yourself absorbing power, love and peace. The supply is limitless.

Imagine yourself becoming charged with health, confidence, creativity and joy.

Picture more white power columns coming down to different areas of your home, including your bed and perhaps your bath, so that you can draw from this energy when you sleep and when you bathe.

Create similar power columns in your place of work and in every part of your world.

If it helps you to do so, then imagine this light coming from The Universal Intelligence, the collective consciousness or God. Whatever fits your beliefs and needs.

This exercise is especially useful for speeding up the recuperative process, combatting fatigue or depression and building confidence.

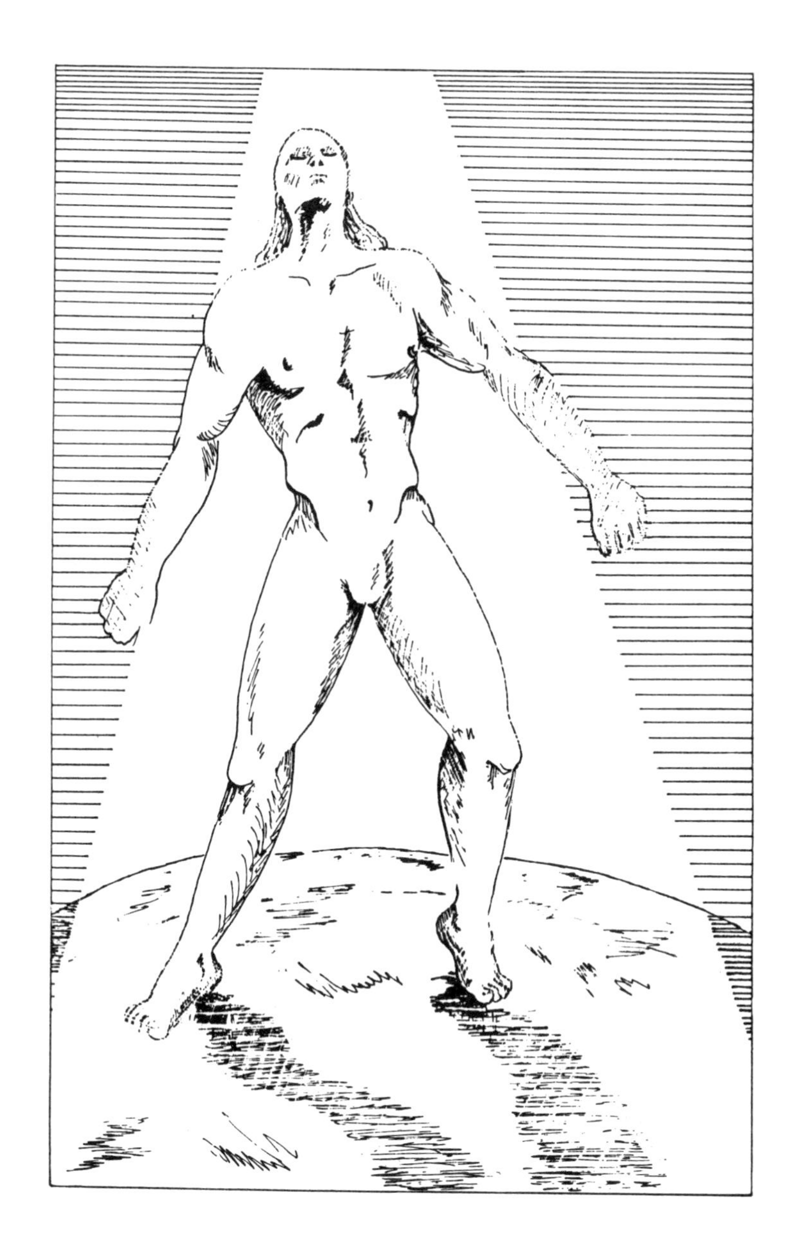

I
PROTECT
MY HEALTH

There are times when it is appropriate for us to be open and vulnerable so that we can enjoy real intimacy with friends, partners, lovers and family.

I believe that being vulnerable is the state of being open to the limitless supply of good things available to us. We need to be able to feel and allow in the love that is there for us. However, it is equally important to learn how to protect ourselves when we choose so that we do not pick up other peoples' negative energy or become drained and therefore open to illness.

In situations where we are surrounded by many people, it is a good idea to use images that keep our energy bright and contained.

Here are three exercise to use to protect yourself. Alternatively you could use the closing down part of the flower exercise on page 26.

A) Imagine yourself drawing down a column of white light energy as in the previous exercise and surrounding the whole of your body with light. Slowly see the column retreating leaving you with an aura of white around every part of you, even under your feet. See the whiteness becoming thicker and more dense around the edges and forming a protective film.

In your mind's eye, picture any negative thought or experience bouncing off this coating while positive experiences are able to move through easily and naturally.

B) Choose a colour that you feel is healing and protective for you at this time; your first thought is usually the best. See yourself putting on a large cloak in your chosen colour. It is long and covers the whole of your body including your feet. The sleeves are long enough to fall over your hands and it has a large hood which you pull over your head. See yourself as safe and protected.

C) Picture yourself enclosed in a large eggshell. Perhaps see yourself physically building it with your hands and painting it with the colour of your choice.

See yourself spraying little ripples of silver or gold over the shell's main colour and imagine good vibrations being able to reach you easily through these marbled areas while you remain completely protected from everything else.

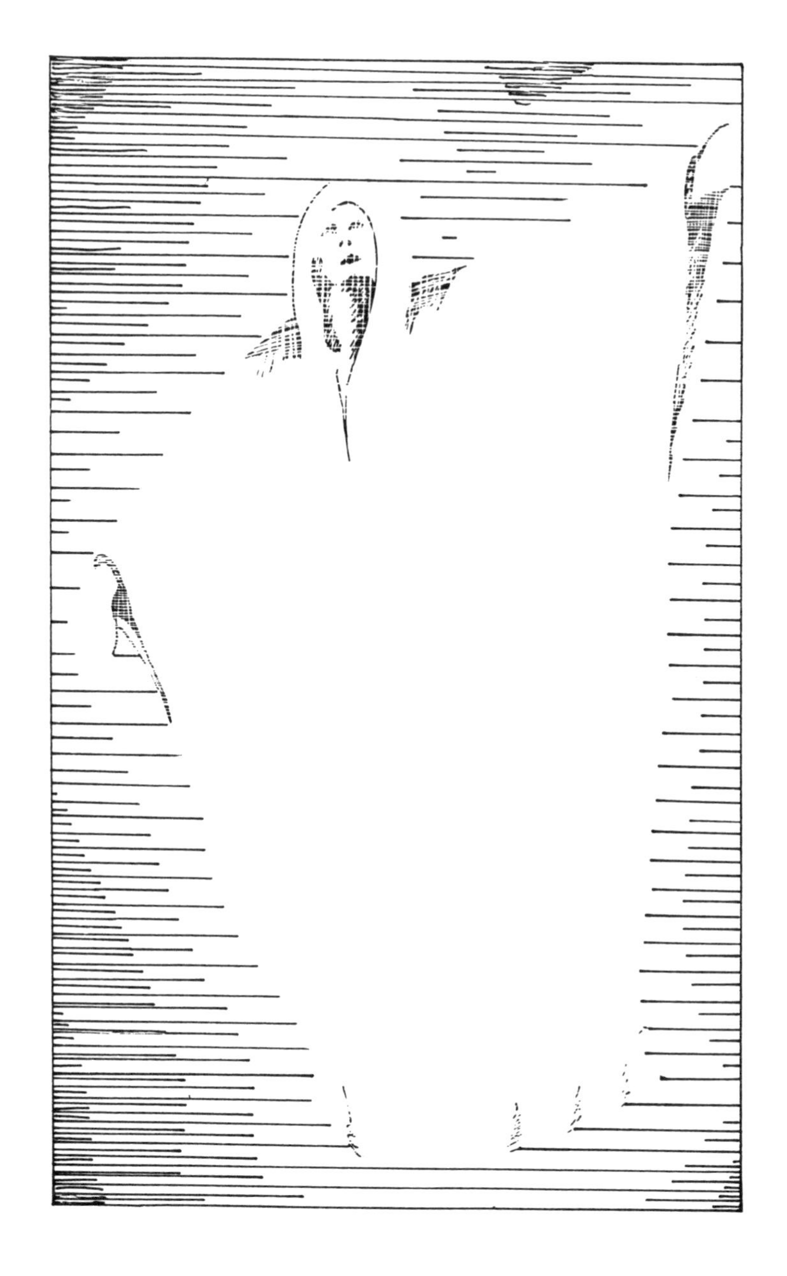

YOUR SELF CARE PROGRAMME

The more we love and care for ourselves the healthier we are. Think for a moment about how much time you currently devote to giving yourself pleasure, pampering yourself and taking care of your health; acknowledge yourself for everything that you already do and know that there is always space for more personal care and self healing.

Find a pen and paper or turn to the 'notes' pages overleaf and put together a plan for your self care programme.

Write a list of things that you can do for yourself every day. Include everything that you currently do and see how many others you can add.

Write a list of things that you can do for yourself every week. Consider how you might alter your weekly schedule to support your health and pleasure.

Write a list of things that you can do for yourself every month. The more you take care of yourself the easier it is to love and care for others.

On the following page you will find some examples, but you might like to explore the alternative therapies available to you within your locality and experiment with some of them. Regularly try something new! Next, take out your diary and book yourself specific times to do as many of these things as you can over the next two months. If any of them need arranging then either do that now or ensure that you also book yourself the time to organise them. Remember that you deserve to have these positive experiences in your life.

Of course, not everything that you do to pamper yourself need cost money, but do consider what you regularly spend on such items as car maintenance or household repairs and decide whether these are more, or less important than investing in your health.

EXAMPLES

EVERY DAY

Take a bath using your favourite oils.
Meditate and use visualisation.
Eat healthy food that you enjoy.
Go for walks - preferably somewhere green.
Take time for your own exercise programme
- Yoga or Tai Chi perhaps.

EVERY WEEK

Have a regular massage (shiatsu, aromatherapy, deep tissue).
Visit a reflexologist.
Book in for a regular hair appointment.
Take an afternoon off to read, write, paint, draw or do whatever you enjoy but don't always give yourself time for, even if you choose to do nothing.

EVERY MONTH

Book time with an acupuncturist or chiropractor for a full body maintenance session.
Have an appointment with your local hands-on or spiritual healer or sit in a regular healing circle. You do not have to be ill to benefit from healing!
How about spending the occasional weekend on a Health Farm?

NOTES

NOTES

NOTES

READING LIST

There are many excellent books available that deal with all aspects of self care and personal development. Here are a few of my personal favourites:

Self Healing and Affirmations

You Can Heal Your Life	by Louise L. Hay*
Heal Your Body	by Louise L. Hay*
Love Your Body	by Louise L. Hay*

Visualisation

Creative Visualisation	by Shakti Gawain

Healers and Healing

I Fly Out with Bright Feathers	by Allegra Taylor
Self Healing My Life & Vision	by Meir Schneider
The Seven Levels of Healing	by Lilla Bek and Philippa Pullar

Inspiration

Illusions	by Richard Bach
Living in the Light	by Shakti Gawain

* Available from Healing Workshops

HEALING WORKSHOPS PRESS

OTHER TITLES

I SEE MYSELF IN PERFECT HEALTH

Audio tapes

Combining some of the visual images from I SEE MYSELF IN PERFECT HEALTH with positive affirmations, David guides you through a series of gentle relaxations designed to promote health and well-being. For home use, these cassettes provide you with a choice of short or long meditations that can become a regular part of your self care programme.

Volume one -

Blue Healing Power/Body Affirmations/Cave of Crystals.
An exploration of images for mental, physical and emotional health.

Volume two -

Magic Carpet/Rainbow colours/Pool of illusions.
A magical journey into colour and self-healing power.

On both tapes David Lawson's voice is perfectly complemented with music that has been especially composed by Paul Chousmer.

Price £ 5.95 each.

MONEY AND YOUR LIFE
A Prosperity Playbook
by
JUSTIN CARSON & DAVID LAWSON

Prosperity is the freedom and pleasure that money can bring. A prosperous person is free and open to unlimited possibilities.

Justin and David guide you through a series of exercises, affirmations and creative daydreams designed to enhance your view of your life and the money in it. Choose the thoughts that draw prosperity to you and fully enjoy the gifts that life has to offer.

"Justin Carson and David Lawson have written a fun and profitable book on the power of affirmations in money management."

- LOUISE L. HAY,
author of YOU CAN HEAL YOUR LIFE

Price £5.95

Also

MONEY AND YOUR LIFE
A Prosperity audio tape
by
JUSTIN CARSON & DAVID LAWSON

Justin and David talk you through some of the exercises and creative daydreams from their Prosperity playbook. An excellent companion to the book, this cassette is designed for you to use at home to help you choose the thoughts that draw prosperity to you. It acts as a personal prosperity workshop for your development.

Price £5.95

OTHER TITLES

YOU CAN HEAL YOUR LIFE VIDEO Study Course

Featuring LOUISE L. HAY

Based on the bestselling book by Louise L. Hay, this VHS video featuring Louise is designed for you to practice the principles of self worth, and self esteem as taught by this Internationally famous Metaphysical teacher.

In the privacy of your own home you can learn to change negative self beliefs and thoughts into positive loving ones. Allow Louise to guide you through exercises and affirmations that teach you to love yourself and change your life.

The video lasts for lO4 minutes.

"I do not heal anyone. I teach people to love themselves and as they learn to love and appreciate who they are, wonderful changes occur for them." - Louise L. Hay

Price £ 23.OO

HOW TO ORDER

Prices of all products are correct at time of going to press and may vary from time to time.

Please add £1.OO post and packing for one item (£1.5O for the video) plus 5Op per additional item.
(Enquire for overseas postal rates).

Please make Cheques, Postal Orders, and International Money orders Payable to **Healing Workshops** and send with your order to

Healing Workshops
PO Box 1678
London NW5 4EW
United Kingdom

Telephone orders with Visa or Mastercard are acceptable, please 'phone (071) 482 4049. Allow 28 days for delivery.

- ABOUT THE AUTHOR -

David Lawson was born in Northamptonshire, England in 1964. Originally training as an actor, his close contact performance pieces and drama workshops led him to train in counselling and run personal development courses.

His popular and unique style of leadership and work with individuals combines spiritual healing, creative programming, meditation, sound & colour work and shamanism. He also helps people to develop their own prosperity, creativity and healing gifts.

In 1987 he spent some time in New York studying the healing circles that have developed as a response to aids and also visiting individual healers and trance mediums.

David directly channels some of the exercises that he uses in workshops, books and tapes.

Editor **Justin Carson** was born in London in 1954. His career has ranged from teaching and social work to organising International Youth Music Festivals and being the Director of a successful Property Company.

His work in healing started in 1984, since when he has directed many people to the discovery of their innate healing powers and their ability to heal their own lives. He recently decided to devote himself full time to healing and leading personal development programmes.

Justin has travelled extensively around the world, having visited 34 different countries at the last count, learning something new in each one.

David and Justin have been working together since 1987. In the summer of 1989 they studied with Louise L. Hay whose metaphysical teachings and writings are now world famous.

Illustrator **Bill Wyatt** is a fine artist living and working in central London where he exhibits regularly. His work encompasses dramatic use of colour, images and styles. Anyone interested in viewing or commissioning artwork can contact Bill through **Healing Workshops.**

Justin Carson & David Lawson

HEALING WORKSHOPS

From their base in London, David and Justin run a variety of courses. These include:

You Can Heal Your Life Study Groups: Run regularly, these study groups based on the best-selling book by Louise L. Hay, encourage you to look at the changes you would like to make in your life and to discover the positive thoughts and tools for change that suit your needs.

Healing Circle: Run on a weekly basis, the healing circle is designed to teach participants how to relax, accelerate recuperation and create an attitude of mind that prevents illness and disease. It is an informal drop-in group that anyone can attend.

Prosperity Day: This is a fun one day workshop filled with exercises and games designed to help change your thoughts on money and abundance so that you create a more prosperous view of your life.

For details of the above, and all future events please write to:

Healing Workshops
PO Box 1678
London NW5 4EW

Or telephone (071) 482 4049.